RTTY and P

for Radio Amateurs

2nd edition

Roger Cooke, G3LDI

CONTENTS

Radio Society of Great Britain

Published by the Radio Society of Great Britain, 3 Abbey Court, Fraser Road, Priory Business Park, Bedford MK44 3WH

First published 2009

Second edition 2013

Reprinted 2014 & 2015

ISBN 9781 9050 8688 7

Publisher's note
The opinions expressed in this book are those of the author and not necessarily those of the RSGB. While the information presented is believed to be correct, the author, publisher and their agents cannot accept responsibility for consequences arising from any inaccuracies or omissions.

Cover design: Kevin Williams, RSGB
Typography and design: Mike Dennison, G3XDV, Emdee Publishing
Production: Mark Allgar, M1MPA, RSGB

Printed in Great Britain by Page Bros Ltd of Norwich

Introduction

T HE APPEAL OF DATA MODES IS the fascination of using coded modes sent from a keyboard and received on a video display. RTTY has been the mainstay of data operating within amateur radio now for well over 50 years. It started in the USA in the mid 1940s, when surplus teleprinters became available and enterprising amateurs bought them and got them working. In the early days the teleprinter was the only means of operating data.

RTTY didn't reach the UK until the late 1950s and the mode was frowned upon by both the CW and the phone operators. I say 'phone' because it was mainly AM (amplitude modulation) in those days. It wasn't until the 1960s that SSB began to take over.

However, with the advent of the computer, the software writers got to work and designed software RTTY, making the teleprinter redundant. Then AMTOR (AMateur Teleprinting Over Radio) came along, courtesy of Peter Martinez, G3PLX, who also went on to produce PSK31. Hence this book covers both RTTY and PSK31. AMTOR seems to have declined in popularity in recent years.

RTTY had a unique attraction because it involved combining both radio and the electromechanical teleprinter. The on-air FSK transmission has an appealing 'jingle-bells' sound to it, with the rapid keying of two tones.

There were considerable technical problems to overcome which also added to the attraction. For most of the older fraternity, such as myself, it started with

Fig 1: The author's modern teledata station

the tracking down of teleprinters, trawling junk yards to look for 'gold dust', and we found them often! I remember opening the back of a derelict old truck and seeing many wooden crates inside. On unscrewing the top of one crate, there wrapped in greased thick paper and stored in wood shavings was a well oiled Creed 7B. My friends and I were like children in a sweet shop! The job of making these machines work and hooking them up to our transmitters took time and patience, but we were well rewarded by our first contacts over the air.

The users also had to learn to type; hunting and pecking was laboriously slow. And teleprinters could be very noisy! Chatting on these data modes can be done in relative silence these days, with the teleprinter having been replaced by the home computer.

Chatting on PSK31 is even better because the use of low power is encouraged. With PSK31, the signal just needs to be a little above the noise and copy is good. The combination of narrow bandwidth, an efficient DSP algorithm and synchronized sampling creates a mode that can be received at very low signal levels, rivalling the weak-signal performance of CW. It is a vast improvement over RTTY. For the same error rate, PSK will get through with several decibels less power than FSK, so PSK is ideal for low power operators.

Bandwidth is another consideration. RTTY, now with 170Hz shift, still occupies around 200Hz. So, within a 3kHz bandwidth around 15 RTTY stations can operate reasonably comfortably. With PSK31, in the same bandwidth, 70 stations can theoretically operate.

Try them both; they both have their advantages and disadvantages. Most amateurs think that RTTY is by far the most suitable mode for contesting and DX-peditions, whereas PSK31 is a mode suitable for chatting. You only have to listen around on the HF bands to prove that theory!

This edition has been revised, and additional material added, to enhance both the understanding and operating of RTTY and PSK31. Enhancements include a more detailed description of both modes and how to use them on the air. It is aimed at the beginner to data modes as experience shows that those attempting to use data for the first time often need a helping hand. For instance, even tuning in a signal is fraught with problems! Hopefully this book will help to dispel some of the mystery. Have fun!

RTTY and PSK31: a brief history

L ANDLINE TELEPRINTER OPERATIONS originally began in 1849 when a circuit was put in service between Philadelphia and New York City. Then, in 1874 Emile Baudot designed a system using a 5-bit code, with equal on and off intervals, which allowed telegraph transmission of the alphabet together with punctuation and control signals. Radioteletype evolved from these earlier landline teleprinter operations.

Commercial RTTY systems were in active service between San Francisco and Honolulu as early as April 1932 and between San Francisco and New York City by 1934. The US Military used radioteletype in the 1930s and expanded this usage during World War II.

Teleprinter system design was gradually improved until, at the beginning of World War II, it represented the principal distribution method used by the news services. The Navy called radioteletype RATT (Radio Automatic TeleType) and the Army Signal Corps called radioteletype SCRT, an abbreviation of Single-Channel Radio Teletype.

The military used frequency shift keying (FSK) and this technology proved very reliable even over long distances. The shift in most common use was 850Hz although other shifts, such as 450Hz were also used. The principle of FSK is described later in this chapter.

Evolution of the ITA2 code

The Baudot Code only described the operator interface, not the method of transmission of the signals down the line. This became known as ITA1 and was quite different from the code we use today.

In 1901, Donald Murray modified ITA1 to reduce the wear and tear on the machinery. This used the start-stop scheme which we know today, eventually becoming known as ITA2 and sometimes referred to as the Murray code. The only common feature between the two systems is that both used a 5-element code. ITA2 (see Note below) is the code used in RTTY communications.

RTTY is known as asynchronous transmission in which a start signal is sent prior to each character and a stop signal is sent after each character. The start signal serves to prepare the receiving mechanism for the reception and the stop

---

NOTE: The 5-unit, start-stop, International Telegraph Alphabet No 2, code defined in International Telegraph and Telephone Consultative Committee Recommendation F.1, Division C is the 5-level code derived from the Murray code. (commonly known as Baudot).

The International Telegraph Alphabet is a result of a joint agreement between the International Telegraph and Telephone Consultative Committee (CCITT), now ITU-T, of the International Telecommunication Union (ITU) and the International Organization for Standardization (ISO).

signal serves to bring the receiving mechanism to rest in preparation for the reception of the next character.

The code used for RTTY is examined in detail in the next chapter.

RTTY

After World War II, amateur radio operators in the USA started to receive obsolete but usable Teletype Model 26 equipment from commercial sources with the understanding that this equipment would not be used for, or returned to, commercial service. Interest increased and soon there was a lot of activity on the two metre band mainly using AFSK keying. Eventually moves were made to use RTTY on the HF bands and one of the prime movers in this respect was Merrill Swan, W6AEE, among others. Merrill was also involved with a publication for RTTY enthusiasts that became *The RTTY Journal*. Amateurs were licensed to use 850Hz FSK on the HF bands with CW identification at the beginning and the end of each transmission and at ten minute intervals.

Most amateurs today will be able to recognise the characteristic 'Jingle Bells' sound of RTTY. This is frequency shift keying (FSK), a frequency modulation scheme in which digital information is transmitted through discrete frequency changes of a carrier wave. The simplest FSK is binary FSK (BFSK) which uses a couple of discrete frequencies to transmit binary (0s and 1s) information. With this scheme, the '1' is called the Mark frequency and the '0' is called the Space frequency. Keying these two frequencies at the normal RTTY speed produced its characteristic sound.

RTTY is now a commonly found mode on the amateur bands. This was not the case in the 1950s as there was no activity in Europe, but it had become commonplace in the USA. In 1959, Arthur "Doc" Gee, G2UK, and Bill Brennan, G3CQE, were two of the first UK stations to use RTTY, or Radioteleype as it was known then.

BARTG (known then as the British Amateur Radio Teletype Group) was formed in 1959 (**Fig 1**). The word Teletype, a trade name of the Teletype Corporation was being used on the *BARTG Newsletters* and in deference to a request the name was changed to the British Amateur Radio Teledata Group.

The Creed 3X tape machine was the first teleprinter to be used and this was soon replaced by the better page printer, the Creed 7B (**Fig 2**). Obtaining the teleprinters became an art form, with many visits to junk yards where model 7Bs were found in large wooden crates, and in very good condition, for about £7.

Fig 1: BARTG's logo

In order to use the teleprinter it was necessary to construct or obtain a 'terminal unit' (TU) as it was called. The teleprinter was originally designed to be used on land-line circuits and communication was achieved by switching on the line in two logic levels called Mark and Space. The native mode of communication for a teleprinter is a simple series DC circuit that is interrupted. The Marking condition is when the circuit is closed (current is flowing), the Spacing condition is when the circuit is open (no current is flowing). Each land-line circuit had a terminal unit, normally involving a polar relay to do the switching.

A different kind of terminal unit was required when connecting the teleprinter to radio equipment. Sometimes called the modem, the TU is an electronic device which is connected between the teleprinter and the radio transceiver. The transmitting part of the modem converts the digital signal transmitted by the

teleprinter to one or the other of a pair of audio frequency tones. One of the tones corresponds to the Mark condition and the other to the Space condition. These audio tones modulate an SSB transmitter to produce the final audio frequency shift keying (AFSK) radio frequency signal. It might also produce voltages that would allow a transmitter to send FSK (frequency shift keying).

Most of the terminal unit equipment used for receiving RTTY signals was homebuilt, using designs published in amateur radio

Fig 2: The Creed 7B teleprinter

publications. These original designs can be divided into two classes of terminal units: audio-type and intermediate frequency converters. The audio-type converters proved to be more popular with amateur radio operators. The Twin City, W2JAV and W2PAT designs are examples of typical terminal units that were used into the middle 1960s. The late 1960s and early 1970s saw the emergence of terminal units designed by W6FFC, such as the TT/L-2, ST-3, ST-5, and ST-6 (**Fig 3**). These designs were first published in the *RTTY Journal* starting in September 1967 and ending in 1970. In the 1960s Byron Kretzman, W2JTP, published a book in the USA called *The RTTY Handbook* in which there was a design of a suitable TU by W2PAT. A number of those were built at the time.

It was necessary to modify the transmitter to allow for HF RTTY operation. This was accomplished by adding a frequency shift keyer that used a diode to switch a capacitor in and out of the circuit, shifting the transmitter's frequency in synchronism with the teleprinter signal changing from Mark to Space to Mark. A small variable capacitor was added to finely adjust the frequency shift.

A very stable transmitter was required for RTTY. The typical frequency multiplication type transmitter that was popular in the 1950s and 1960s would be

Fig 3: Still regarded as a reliable workhorse for machine RTTY, the ST-6 was built in the mid-1070s

relatively stable on 80 meters but become progressively less stable on 40 meters, 20 meters and 15 meters. By the middle 1960s, transmitter designs were updated, mixing a crystal-controlled high frequency oscillator with a variable low frequency oscillator, resulting in better frequency stability across all amateur HF bands.

Bill, G3CQE, put RTTY onto 21MHz and his first contact was with Jim VE7KX who always had a superb signal into the UK. Bill was in great demand on HF as he was the first G station HF RTTY and he had a ball. Most of the contacts were with USA and Canadian stations as they had been active on RTTY for a year or two before us. Bill wrote a column in the *Short Wave Magazine* and soon more British stations became interested. This was 1959, a time when we all used 850Hz shift and had to identify on CW at the end of every transmission!

Note that 850Hz spacing between mark and space frequencies was used because it was the standard shift of that time, with most commercial stations using it so amateurs just followed suit. This was later lowered to 170Hz in order to accommodate the increasing number of stations using RTTY.

Obtaining parts was difficult bearing in mind that the teleprinter is an electro-mechanical device used mainly by commercial organizations. However sources were found for stroboscopes, feeler gauges, tension gauges and so on, not forgetting the oil-can and grease that was also needed!

During the early days of amateur RTTY, the Worked All Continents - RTTY Award was conceived by the RTTY Society of Southern California and issued by the *RTTY Journal*. The first amateur radio station to achieve this Award was Jim Hepburn VE7KX. The first stations recognized as having achieved single band WAC RTTY were W1MX (3.5 MHz); DL0TD (7.0 MHz); K3SWZ (14.0 MHz); W0MT (21.0 MHz) and FG7XT (28.0 MHz). The ARRL began issuing WAC RTTY certificates in 1969.

**Fig 4: The Creed
444 teleprinter**

By the early 1970s, amateur RTTY had spread around the world and it was finally possible to work more than 100 countries via RTTY. FG7XT was the first station to claim to achieve this honor. However, Jean did not submit his QSL cards for independent review. ON4BX, in 1971, was the first station to submit his cards to the DX Editor of the *RTTY Journal* and to achieve the award. The ARRL began issuing DXCC RTTY Awards on November 1, 1976.

Eventually other machines became available, the Creed 75, the 444 (**Fig 4**) and the Teletype Corporation model 19 (**Fig 5**) becoming popular. The 'holy grail' of the RTTY machines was the very rare, in the UK anyway, Model 28 ASR (**Fig 6**).

In the 1980s RTTY mailboxes were set up on HF, mostly on 80 meters. The access was very tenuous to say the least. The transmit frequency had to be within about 10 to 20Hz in order to access, and equipment at that time was not the most stable.

In the 1950s through the 1970s, 'RTTY art' was a popular on-air activity. It consisted of (sometimes very elaborate and artistic) pictures sent via RTTY through the use of lengthy punched tape transmissions and then printed by the

(left) Fig 5: The Teletype model 19 used by the author at the end of his days with mechanical teleprinters

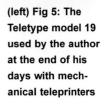

(right) Fig 6: The desirable but rare Western Union model 28 ASR

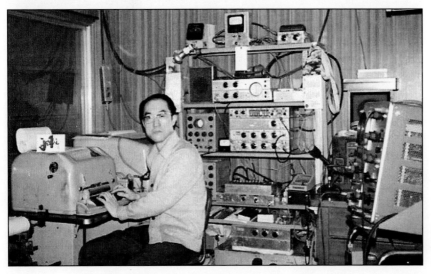

Fig 7: The 1970s RTTY station of JA1DI

receiving station on paper. Sometimes, transmission of a picture could take up to 30 or 40 minutes! This is a long time to transmit 100% duty cycle, but then most amplifiers were in Class C in those days!

To show just what a station would look like some 40 years ago, take a look at the typical station of JA1DI Isao Yamaguchi, Tokyo, Japan - from RTTY QSL dated 1 Mar, 1975, in **Fig 7**.

Another is that of Henry Rogers WA7YBS in **Fig 8**. His station description makes interesting reading:

"In the rack from top to bottom, CV-89A RTTY TU, Dovetron Tempest RTTY TU, CV-116/URR RTTY Diversity TU, Collins R-390A/URR receiver, Dovetron Multipath RTTY TU, patch panel, keying loop supply and at the bottom an eight inch PM speaker with 600-ohm Z-matching transformer. On the shelf (left to right), dual speaker panel on top of a HAL ST-6 RTTY TU, Collins 51J-2 receiver and a Collins 75A-4 receiver. Center floor is the AN/TT-7 FG (model 19) TTY machine and next to it the Collins KWS-1 transmitter. Although all of the gear in the rack does work, I normally used the 75A-4 and KWS-1 as the receiver and transmitter and then demodulated the RTTY with the HAL ST-6. This set-up with the Model 19 TTY worked quite well. The KWS-1 had to be run at reduced power due to the 100% duty-cycle of RTTY but still 200W output provided a decent signal."

Fig 9 shows a keyboard from the Model 19 set. Most teleprinter keyboards were like this, just three rows, each key doubling up. There was an art in just

Fig 8: The superb
1970s station of
RTTY enthusiast
Henry Rogers,
WA7YBS

Fig 9: A typical teleprinter keyboard, famous for its green keys

keying the teleprinter, getting into the actual rhythm of the speed you were using. Just about all teleprinter keys were green, hence the old saying "See you on the green keys".

The G3PLX video RTTY unit

This project was designed by Peter Martinez G3PLX in the 1970s [1]. I built one on a set of veroboards, and the main display was a 12-inch amber-screen portable 12V TV set. **Fig 10** shows a block diagram of a typical amateur RTTY station using a VDU system.

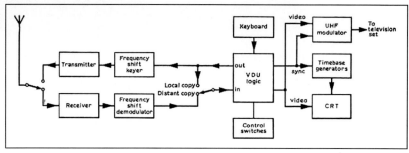

Fig 10: VDU system used before computers made easy work of electronic RTTY

Transmission of RTTY took place using the input from a keyboard and fed to the transmitter at logic levels to key it, with input to the VDU unit in order to monitor the outgoing message. The VDU displayed 24 lines of text with 40 characters per line. This conflicts with the normal 70 characters per line of a teleprinter, but this was due to the definition limitations of the normal 625 line TV set.

This was quite a complicated construction project and even in 1977 the chips came to around £50 in total! I seem to remember that the keyboard was about £10 or so. You can pick up a brand new computer keyboard now for around £2.00! However, this unit worked a lot of DX and lasted until the computer came along and changed everything. RTTY was finally a quiet mode!

Computers

When the personal computer came into amateurs' shacks, these replaced the mechanical teleprinter for good. The popular BBC-B computer, together with the Nascom, Sinclair ZX81/Spectrum and the Commodore 64 paved the way for the ubiquitous PC that most shacks possess today.

The teleprinter has mostly been confined to history. However, if you haven't seen one working, please do try to do so. They really are fascinating to watch.

PSK

In the 1990s, Peter Martinez, G3PLX, had already established himself firmly on the data scene with his very popular AMTOR mode. AMTOR, which started in 1978, is an amateur usage of the ARQ scheme invented by Van Duuren of the Dutch equivalent of the British Diplomatic Wireless Service around 1970. Peter

Fig 11: A typical
modern PSK31
program. The
'waterfall' display
at the bottom
shows the received
signals

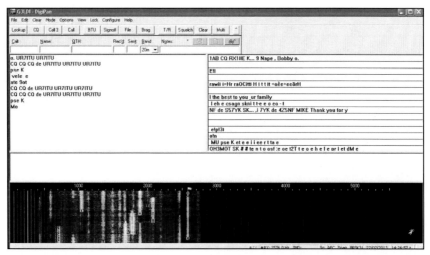

coined the name AMTOR to avoid the problems with using the trade-names Sitor or Spector by which this system became widely known.

The term AMTOR is an acronym for AMateur Teleprinting Over Radio. It improves on RTTY by incorporating a simple error detection technique. The system remains relatively uncomplicated but AMTOR performs well even in poor HF conditions. While there can still be many errors in AMTOR data, the error detection helps a lot and the result is quite tolerable for normal text mode conversations because of the high redundancy in plain language text. It is much better than RTTY but sends only three characters at a time and waits for a response, or 'handshake', so is quite reliant on a fast changeover time of the transceiver.

It is a fascinating mode to use, though not heard much these days. Probably the punishing use of the transmit/receive relays was the reason for the fading of the AMTOR's popularity.

In 1998, Peter turned his attention to a mode called PSK31. Instead of using FSK (Frequency Shift Keying) as RTTY does, this mode uses PSK (Phase Shift Keying). It uses an alphabet dictionary similar to Morse, allowing a larger character set and giving a text speed of about 50WPM (words per minute). Like RTTY it does not employ handshaking, and tuning is made quite simple with most computer programs providing a 'waterfall' type display (**Fig 11**).

Other amateurs have developed a double-speed version of PSK31, universally known as PSK63, and a quadruple speed version as PSK125. Lower speed versions have also been developed for use on the LF bands. PSK31 is essentially a chat mode and is not really suitable for contesting.

Just like RTTY, early experiments involved the use of a specialised PSK modem, but they became redundant again as numerous computer programs became available. It is possible to run any data mode on a modern PC, making life a lot quieter.

Reference

[1]   'The G3PLX Mk 2 RTTY Video Display Unit', J P Martinez, G3PLX, *RadCom* April. 1977, RSGB

2

Basic RTTY theory

SINCE THE FIRST EDITION OF this book, I have given several talks to radio clubs about getting started in both RTTY and PSK, and it is obvious that some more basic theory is needed in order for the beginner to understand the nuances associated with both modes.

Starting with RTTY then, although the teleprinter has lost prominence in the amateur radio station, there are still those using machines of various types. This basic theory will apply whatever method you use to encode and decode RTTY signals.

There are other books available to cover in great detail the mechanics of the machines so a few pictures is all that I shall show here. One such book is *The Teleprinter Handbook*, first published by the RSGB in 1973 and still available on the second hand market.

The teleprinter was originally designed to be used on land-line circuits and communication was achieved by switching between two logic levels called Mark and Space. The native mode of communication for a teleprinter is a simple series DC circuit that is interrupted. The Marking condition is when the circuit is closed (current is flowing), the Spacing condition is when the circuit is open (no current is flowing).

The 'idle' condition of the circuit is a continuous Marking state, with the start of a character signalled by a 'start bit', which is always a Space. Following the start bit, the character is represented by a fixed number of bits, such as the five bits in the Baudot code, each either a mark or a space to denote the specific character or machine function. After the character's bits, the sending machine sends one or more stop bits. The stop bits are Marking, so as to be distinct from the subsequent start bit. **Fig 12** shows a single letter in Marks and Spaces.

If the sender has nothing more to send, the line simply remains in the Marking state (as if a continuing series of stop bits) until a later space denotes the start of the next character. The time between characters need not be an integral multiple of a bit time, but it must be at least the minimum number of stop bits required by the receiving machine.

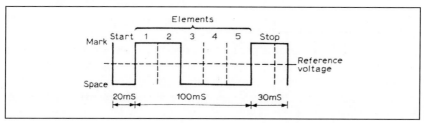

Fig 12: Represent-
ation of the letter
'A' in the 5-bit
Murray code.

Terminal unit

Each landline circuit had a terminal unit, normally involving a polar relay to do the switching. The terminal unit (TU) is still required when connecting the teleprinter to a transceiver.

The terminal unit is an electronic device which is connected between the teleprinter (more frequently a computer nowadays) and the radio transceiver. The transmitting part of the modem converts the digital signal transmitted by the teleprinter to one or the other of a pair of audio frequency tones. One of the tones corresponds to the Mark condition and the other to the Space condition. These audio tones modulate an SSB transmitter to produce the final audio-frequency shift keying (AFSK) radio frequency signal. It might also produce voltages that would allow a transmitter to send FSK (frequency shift keying).

These days, we rarely refer to a 'terminal unit' but more usually an interface or modem.

Some modern transceivers have RTTY as a built in feature, so no external interface is required. Bear in mind however, that this is fine for casual operating, but it would still pay to use an interface and a computer program if operating seriously in contests.

The code

On the amateur HF bands, the 5-bit Murray code is used, meaning that every character consists of five bits, either mark or space; it is actually 8 bits because a start bit and one and a half stop bits are added for synchronization.

Take a look at the representation of the letter A in Fig 12. It can be seen that 'A' consists of two Marks followed by three spaces with a 20mS start bit and a 30mS stop bit.

The five data bits allow for only 32 different codes, which cannot accommodate the 26 letters, 10 figures, space, a few punctuation marks and the required control codes, such as carriage return, new line, bell, etc. To overcome this limitation, the teleprinter has two states, the un-shifted or 'letters' state and the shifted or 'numbers' or 'figures' state. The change from one state to the other takes place when the special control codes LETTERS and FIGURES are sent from the keyboard or received from the line. In the 'letters' state the teleprinter prints the letters and space while in the shifted state it prints the numerals and punctuation marks.

With normal operation of RTTY, a rate of 45.45 bauds is used on HF. The term 'baud' originates from the French engineer Emile Baudot, who invented the 5-bit teletype code. Baud rate refers to the number of signal or symbol changes that occur per second. 45.45 bauds is the equivalent of 60WPM.

In the UK, during the mechanical era, the standard was 50 bauds. Changing speeds entailed a change of the governor or the use of a stroboscope to adjust the governor on the teleprinter motor. This took time and was really problematic, especially if the teleprinter had a silence cover.

Even though 45.45 bauds is the accepted standard today, you will occasionally come across an RTTY signal at a different speed. Changing speeds within software is so much easier now and higher speeds can sometimes be heard.

As Chairman of BARTG I have managed to rejuvenate the use of 75 bauds with two short, four hour 75 baud contests per year, one in April and the second in September. These are increasing in popularity and there is a lot of activity in both, given propagation. It might not sound much of a change, from 45.45 to 75 bauds, but the higher speed certainly does require concentration and a skilled use of the keyboard. The days of 'hunt and peck' have long since gone!

Error correction

RTTY is not an error correction mode; there is no handshaking protocol in use, so a reasonable signal is required for good copy. Fortunately, most modern transceivers have catered for the use of RTTY and have excellent filters, AGC systems and digital signal processing (DSP) to cope with most conditions found on HF, so copy is normally very good, even if the signal is weak.

Good copy is also heavily dependant on proper receiver adjustments, plus the quality of the computer program in use at the time too, of course.

Duty cycle

The other major point to remember about RTTY is that it is a 100% duty cycle mode. In other words your transmitter is keyed all the time, so you must remember to reduce the power level. If you have a 100 watt transceiver for example, reduce the power to about 75 watts to preserve the PA. This is particularly important if you are having a normal chatty type contact with transmission periods lasting a few minutes. Try to ensure that the SWR is 1:1, or as near to it as you can get, as this will also help.

Tones and shift

The standard mark and space tones are 2125Hz and 2295Hz respectively. These tones are also referred to as 'high' tones. These are the standard tones used to produce 170Hz shift and are the normal ones in use on HF. Back in the early days we all used 850Hz shift, as did all the commercial and military stations. We merely followed in the same way, using 850Hz.

Shift is the difference in frequency between the two tones, Mark and Space. Most RTTY these days uses 170Hz shift, the narrower standard being introduced to accommodate the increased number of stations as RTTY became more popular.

There are two ways of transmitting RTTY. These are FSK (frequency-shift keying) and AFSK (audio-frequency-shift keying). Most operators prefer FSK as it produces a much cleaner signal, free from harmonics and IMD products sometimes apparent on an AFSK signal.

FSK

FSK is a frequency modulation scheme in which digital information is transmitted through frequency changes of a carrier wave. The simplest form is binary FSK (BFSK). This literally implies using a couple of discrete frequencies to transmit binary (0s and 1s) information. With this scheme, the '1' is called the Mark frequency and the '0' is called the Space frequency. FSK can be applied directly to any of the transmitter's oscillators, but most modern transceivers today have an FSK input. This takes a binary DC keying voltage from an interface or a computer's serial COM port (with the *MMTTY* software you can also use a parallel LPT port to transmit FSK) and uses it to change the transmitter's

Fig 13: Frequency
shift keying (FSK):
Binary data (a)
frequency
modulates the
carrier to produce
the FSK signal (b)
which has the
frequency
characteristic (c)

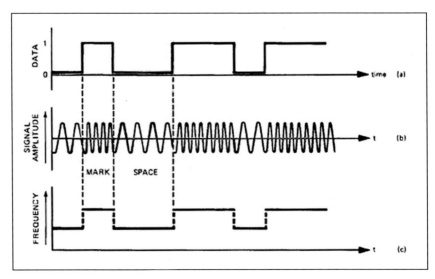

output frequency by an amount equal to the shift. On receive, the radio may be operated in the 'RTTY' or 'FSK' position which make use of narrow 250Hz or 500Hz IF filters. FSK is shown in **Fig 13**. The two binary states, logic 0 (low) and 1 (high), are each represented by an analog waveform. Logic 0 is represented by a wave at a specific frequency, and logic 1 is represented by a wave at a different frequency.

AFSK

AFSK is when you send audio from an interface or sound card to the audio input of your transmitter. This can be either via the microphone input or accessory jack, which can usually be found on the back of your transceiver. Convention dictates that when using AFSK, your radio will be placed in the LSB (Lower Side Band) position. In general, it is important to keep the audio drive low enough so that the transmitter does not generate any ALC voltage.

Unlike FSK, AFSK can be used on an FM transmitter.

Confusion with AFSK tones and dials

Imagine you want to transmit on 14080kHz. Your Mark signal has to be on 14080kHz. With your transmitter in the LSB mode, whatever frequency goes into the microphone input will be subtracted from what your dial says and be transmitted on that frequency. Therefore, if your dial says 14080kHz and you put in a 1000Hz audio tone, your transmitter will put out an RF signal at 14079kHz; exactly 1000Hz lower than your dial. So in this case, if the 1000Hz represented your Mark signal, you would have to set your transmitter to '14081' on the dial, and your Mark signal would be transmitted on 14080kHz, just as you wanted. The space frequency will be transmitted 170Hz lower, on 14079.83kHz. The audio tone that will give you 14079.83 is 14081 minus 14079.83, or 1170Hz. So the mark audio frequency is 1000Hz and space is 1170Hz.

There you have the basics of AFSK. Audio frequencies are injected into the microphone input and your transmitter converts them into two RF frequencies. For technical reasons related to harmonic generation, audio frequencies of

1000Hz and 1170Hz are *not* recommended. They are used in this example just to keep the maths simple. The frequencies used are 2125Hz for the mark audio frequency and 2295Hz for the space audio frequency. Making the frequencies higher like this will mean that the filter in the SSB transmitter will reduce any spurious emissions that might be caused by the second harmonic of the audio tones.

The space audio frequency is higher than the mark audio frequency - just the opposite of the RF frequency you actually transmit. This happens because you are using lower sideband. If you happen to forget and set your transmitter to USB instead of LSB, two things will happen. Because your mark and space are now reversed in your receiver, any RTTY signals you hear will not display correctly. All you will see is random characters that make no sense at all. This is commonly referred to as being 'upside-down'. The other thing is that *your* transmissions will also be nonsense to the other guy, so just remember - always use LSB. If you see garbage and are tuned correctly, look for a button within your RTTY program called REV (reverse), or just switch from upper sideband to lower.

To diddle or not to diddle!

To increase reception accuracy, the answer is to 'diddle'! Here's why.

Even though Baudot is a five bit character code, three extra bits are added to provide character synchronization. A start bit (Space tone) is prepended to the Baudot code, and two stop bits (Mark tone) are added after the Baudot code. Thus the actual character is 8 bits.

In 'rest' or idle condition, RTTY sends a continuous Mark tone. After an idle (Mark) period, the Baudot stream decoder will wait for the first space tone to be demodulated. The decoder assumes this is a Start bit, then it assumes that the tone 1/45.45 seconds later represents the first bit of the Baudot character, and the one 2/45.45 seconds later represents the second bit of the Baudot character, and so on.

After sending the five bits of the character, you send a stop sequence (two bit periods, in the case of amateur RTTY) to place the system back into the idle state, so the Baudot decoder can now look for the Start bit of the next character.

However, if you miss the first start bit of the first character after a long idle mark, not only do you miss decoding the first character properly, you will be out of sync for quite a while, mistaking a lot of future data bits as start bits, and advancing the character timing only when the place where a start bit should have fallen happens to have a mark tone.

There is a 50% chance that you will advance after an error, and 50% chance you continue to be out of sync. Even when you advance, you may hit yet another space character that is not a start bit. On average, it takes three to four character periods before you are in sync again.

So, after making a character synchronization error, not only do you mess up decoding that character, you will be printing gibberish for the next couple of characters too, until character sync is accomplished.

This is where the 'diddle' comes in. Diddles are just a non-printing character, usually the Baudot LTRS (letters shift) character. When you transmit diddles, you replace the idle Mark tone by a repeating sequence of LTRS. What really helps is that the Baudot LTRS character is 11111 (all Mark tones). So if you miss a character synchronization of one LTRS character, the Baudot decoder will immediately advance to the next true start bit (Space) since there are no bits in LTRS which looks like a start bit. Software programs allow for 'diddle on' and 'diddle off', so it is simple to implement.

Summary
The following assumes a transceiver frequency displayed as '14080kHz', LSB:
- RTTY transmission is independent of local tones. However, the higher RF frequency is always the Mark, and the lower is the Space.
- The difference between the two frequencies is the shift (170Hz)
- When using FSK the Mark frequency is displayed. In our example, the Mark frequency is 14080.000kHz and the the Space is 14079.830kHz.
- AFSK displays suppressed carrier! For a Mark tone of 2125Hz the transmission is on 14077.875kHz. For a Space tone of 2295Hz, the transmission is on 14077.705kHz.

Where to find RTTY

Originally, RTTY had to find a slot on the amateur bands when there was no other activity. So, the first stations to use the mode decided to pick a spot in between the CW and phone sub-bands. RTTY operators have stayed there ever since. **Table 1** shows where you will find RTTY on each of the HF amateur bands during normal operation and during contests. Note that *no* contesting of any sort is allowed on the 'WARC' bands of 30, 17 and 12m.

The contesting segments mentioned in the table are usually occupied by USA stations during a major contest. It is not normal for UK stations to operate outside their recommended segments. In fact BARTG actively promote staying within the RTTY sub-band.

10m	28080 - 28100kHz	During contests 28050 - 28150kHz
12m	24910 - 24929kHz	NO contesting on this band Most activity around 24920kHz
15m	21080 - 21110kHz	During contests 21060 - 21150kHz
17m	18100 - 18109kHz	NO contesting on this band Occasional activity 18090 - 18100
20m	14080 - 14100kHz	During contests 14060 - 14140kHz
30m	10120 - 10150kHz	NO contesting on this band Most activity around 10140kHz
40m	7040 - 7050kHz	During contests (but not UK) 7025 - 7100kHz) US stations allowed RTTY 7100 - 7125kHz
80m	3580 - 3600kHz	During contests 3570 - 3620kHz Japanese allocation 3520 - 3525kHz US stations not permitted RTTY above 3600kHz
160m	1838 - 1840kHz	During contests 1820 - 1840kHz RTTY is very rare on this band
Avoid PSK frequencies: 28120, 21070, 14070, 7035, 7040, 3580 and 1838kHz.		
Avoid MSK frequencies: 14080 - 14082kHz		
Avoid NCDXF frequencies: 14100, 18110, 21150, 24930, and 28200kHz		

Table 1: Where to find RTTY on the HF bands

3

Let's get started on RTTY

THE BLOCK DIAGRAM (**Fig 14**) shows the various parts that make up a typical modern RTTY (or PSK) station. It is quite different from how things were done in the days of mechanical teleprinters.

Transceiver

Most people will already have an HF radio, but if you don't as yet, then give some serious thought to the one that you want. Obviously price will be a deciding factor, but there are some bargains to be had in the small ads etc. Remember the HF radio is the main item in any HF station so give a lot of thought to your purchase.

You will need a radio that is as modern as possible. If it is a modern radio, it will have good sensitivity, selectivity and stability, essential features for all modes, but even more so for data. It should have selectivity down to 250Hz, and DSP too. If you look at the Icom 7600 or Pro III for example, RTTY is built in and they can be used without an interface, even with split frequency operation (**Fig 15**). However, for serious contesting, it is best to use a computer and a contest program; the facilities are so much greater. Another useful feature is a panoramic display, such as the Pro III has.

It will also preferably have an FSK facility, as this is the preferred method of keying as discussed in the previous chapter. Refer to the manual if you are

Fig 14: How the parts of a typical RTTY station are interconnected

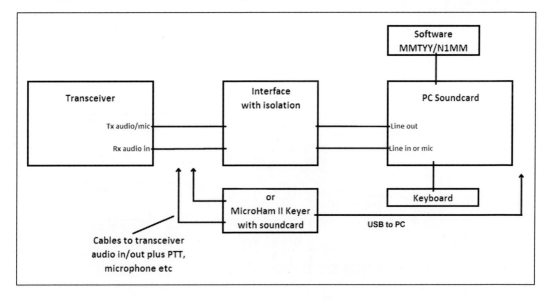

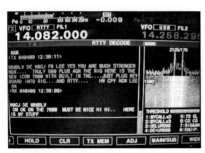

unsure. There will probably be a section in the manual devoted to using the transceiver on RTTY, and datamodes in general.

As a starting point, you should have the radio set in LSB RTTY position, AGC off or fast, with a 500Hz IF filter selected. Keep the power level down to around 75% of normal output.

You can find a comprehensive list of radios suitable for RTTY at [1].

Fig 15: RTTY being received on the Icom 7800 without an interface

Computer

A fairly up to date PC, with a fast processor, USB ports and a suitable sound card if needed, will make life a lot easier than if trying to run on an old machine. Try to avoid Windows Vista if possible, as at the time of writing not all programs will run using that platform, whereas Windows XP or Windows 7 are more compatible. Most shacks these days are very well equipped in this respect as so much amateur radio is computer related and a computer is almost a necessity in a modern shack. It does help to make it a dedicated shack computer.

Unfortunately, most modern PCs do not have a COM port so beware of that when deciding on an interface. There are USB to COM converters available.

A fairly large display will also be needed, set into the middle of your desk as there will be a lot of windows you will need to refer to and the larger the display the better. Soundcards used to present a problem, but a lot of modern interfaces have their own built-in sound card so this is no longer the case.

Interfaces explained

Very simple interfaces can be employed with few components. It depends on how serious you are about using data modes. Start off with a simple one by all means and if the modes appeal to you, it is then possible to upgrade. **Fig 16** gives you an idea of how to interface for either FSK or AFSK.

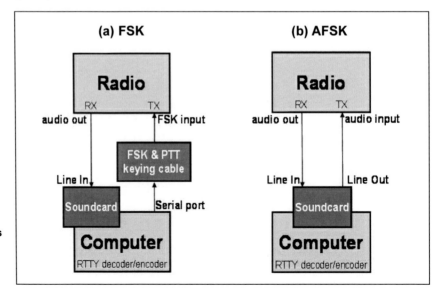

Fig 16: The basics of interfacing for (a) FSK and (b) AFSK

There are many types of interface that are available to connect computers to transceivers (one example is shown below, another is on the CD). These usually work very well and allow you to configure the connections for any type of transceiver and come complete with all the interconnecting leads. However, you can get on the air for a fraction of the price with the simplest of circuits that can be made very quickly. It won't contain the Winkey Morse keyer, or any other bells and whistles, but at least you will be on the air. You can, with only a minimum of components and a home made interface, be active on RTTY.

Interfaces are a personal choice at the end of the day, and some research should be done before deciding which route you wish to take.

Simple home-made interface for RTTY/PSK

Fig 17 shows a fairly simple way to interface a computer soundcard to an HF rig to operate PSK31, SSTV & RTTY. It uses the serial port of the PC, and unfortunately modern PCs don't have serial ports, but converters are available. If you have an older PC with a serial port, this would be a simple one to build. The interface requires no external power, being powered by the serial port.

The circuit consists of an audio transformer, a capacitor, a PC-mount 10k potentiometer, an opto-coupler IC such as a 4N25 or 4N35, a 100 ohm resistor, a 10µF capacitor, and an LED. The optical coupler IC and audio transformers provide isolation between the HF rig and the soundcard.

From Fig 17 you can see that the interface is built in three parts. The top portion shows the audio in from the radio to the computer's sound card. Isolation is provided by a 1:1 audio transformer.

The second part of the circuit shows the transmit audio from the sound card's output to the radio's mic input. A second 1:1 audio transformer is used. The transmit audio level is adjusted using the 10k pot.

The third part shows the PTT function provided by an opto isolator chip which is triggered by a positive voltage on the serial port's RTS line, or pin 7 in

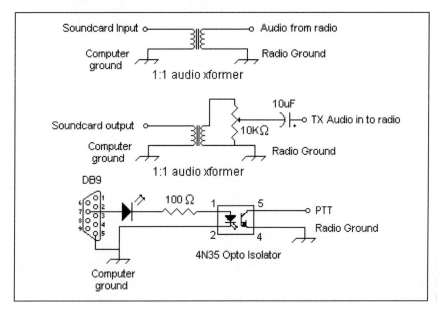

Fig 17: Simple RTTY interface to build

Fig 18: This FSK
interface can be
bought as a kit

Fig 18: This FSK interface can be bought as a kit

the DB9 connector. The voltage is provided by the computer itself, which turns on the LED and opto isolator chip. The LED inside the chip turns on the transistor and keys the PTT line. Pins 3 and 6 have no connection. The second LED can be omitted if you wish, but it is handy to have a visual indicator of when the PTT line is keyed by the computer.

You should refer to your transceiver's manual to determine which pins to make the proper connections to the mic plug.

A useful web site when connections are needed to your transceiver can be seen at [2]. You can even buy ready made cable sets if needed.

Interface in kit form

W3YY's simple FSK/CW Optically Isolated PC Interface (**Fig 18**) comes as a kit to build, complete with a PCB, all parts, mounting hardware and assembly instructions. It will operate from either the serial port or, with an add-on, from a USB port.

Much more information is available on the web page at [3].

Sophisticated commercial interfaces

The MicroHam USB MicroKeyer II

If you are really serious about data modes in general, or even CW and SSB, then if you can afford it, go for something like the MicroHam MicroKeyer II, **Fig19**.

Take a look at the web site at [4] for all the specs and see the CD that accompanies this book for a review I wrote for *RadCom* a few years ago so you can decide for yourself. Several members of my local club, the Norfolk ARC, are now using the MicroHam II and are very pleased they decided to buy it.

The MicroHam II includes a radio control interface that supports all standards (RS-232, CI-V, Kenwood and Yaesu TTL), a powerful CW memory keyer using K1EL's WinKey, two channel audio for transceivers with dual receivers, automatic microphone selection, and a buffer/sequencer for amplifier or LNA control. This device is an all-in-one USB interface and will work with any Windows-based logging or control program for CW, voice, FSK and digital (RTTY, PSK31, SSTV, OLIVIA, MFSK, WSJT, etc.) plus SSB with Digital Voice Keying (DVK). It also has its own built-in sound card, which really does make life easier. This is probably the one to aim for if you want the ultimate in Data interfaces.

Fig 19: A sophisticated commercial datamodes interface

The DigiMaster microFSK Digital Data Interface

Neil Crook, G4ZLP has been marketing interfaces for a number of years and has just produced a novel way of generating FSK. The microFSK allows you to transmit FSK RTTY in a number of formats and *any* user-defined baud rate, including of course *all* of the standard FSK RTTY speeds. It is essentially an add-on unit to give full FSK capability.

Although this unit has been developed for use with the DigiMaster range of interfaces it will function with any interface (if not using a DigiMaster interface you may need to make your own suitable leads).

The mFSK interface was developed and made in the UK, and is a microprocessor based FSK generator. It is connected to the PC and appears to Windows as a simple USB-serial interface. The microprocessor accepts commands to configure it through simple software. Then you simply send characters down the RS232 port that you want your transmitter to send by FSK.

The microprocessor can convert incoming RS232 (at any serial transfer speed) into 5-bit baudot, 7-bit ASCII, 8-bit ASCII, at a baud rate anywhere between 10 - 600Bd, and generates accurately timed FSK signals.

Fig 20: Two views of the microFSK Digital DATA Interface. On the left is the outside of the box as sold, and on the right is a prototype version

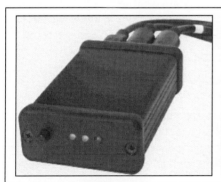

Fig 21: How the microFSK connects to your station

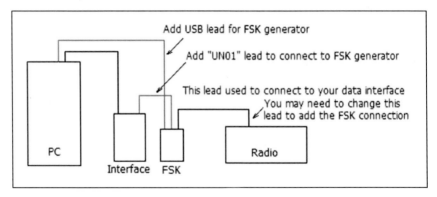

The PCB will connect to a USB port on your PC and will appear as a COM port. You then download the mFSK software. It will also be supported by other software in due course, so there should be compatibility with *MMTTY* for example. Run it and connect to the interface.

Using the software's menu system, configure the interface to the parameters you want to use. Then just type (or cut and paste) into the lower window, click Tx and the interface will key your radio and activate FSK according to your requirements.

Fig 20 shows the interface as sold and a prototype of the microFSK board itself. The connections are in **Fig 21**.

The DigiMaster microFSK Interface module is designed as an add on unit for use with any of the DigiMaster DATA interfaces, but it is claimed to be usable with any data interface.

Full details of the microFSK Interface, and other products by G4ZLP can be found on his web site at [5].

Other commercial interfaces
There are many other similar devices available on the market, such as the Rascal, the RigBlaster, the SignalLink to mention just three. I am just showing the extremes available, as the final choice will be a personal one.

Software
There are many software programs for RTTY and there are many web sites that you can visit, download the software and try it. Some of these are suitable for most modes of operation, DX, chatting, contesting and so on. Others are contest programs only; I will discuss suitable contesting programs in a later chapter. The accompanying CD gives a long list of interesting sites to investigate as well as lots of software.

MMTTY the standard
Again it will be a personal choice but I shall describe one of the most popular programs, *MMTTY*. This is a superb program for general DX or chat use and is free to use. Written by Makoto Mori, JE3HHT, it is included on the CD accompanying this book. Get the latest version from the web [6] or the CD and install it. The downloaded file is a self-extracting and self installing file, so you

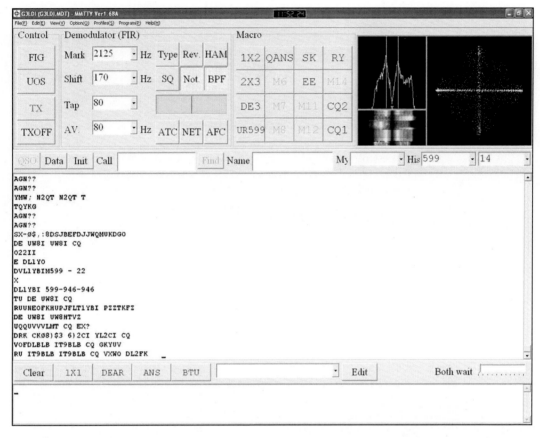

Fig 22: MMTTY in action

should have no problems. Just follow the instructions and accept all the on-screen prompts, not forgetting to make an on-screen Icon. You should end up with a screen display looking like **Fig 22**.

If you are using a commercial interface, the connecting leads are normally included. However, if you use a home-made one, you will need to interface to the soundcard in the PC. There is a lot of information in the Help file of *MMTTY* and even more on the web site at [7]. There is an excellent tutorial and full set-ting-up instructions on Don, AA5AU's web site [8]. This site has a huge amount of tutorial information.

Setting up a program like *MMTTY* can be confusing at first so do take a look at the Help file and perhaps print it out for future reference. Once you have browsed the entire help file and hopefully read most of it, you will then be ready to hook up your sound card to your radio to receive RTTY.

If you do have problems, don't forget that you can always ask! The best place to ask is the MMTTY User's Group on Yahoo. You can access this User's Group by going to the Help pull-down menu within *MMTTY* and select 'MMTTY User's Group'. Choosing this option will open up your web browser to where you can join the User's Group. Alternatively do a search at [9].

You can also join BARTG [10] for free. A lot of the members use *MMTTY*, which is the most popular RTTY program in use today, so you will be in good company.

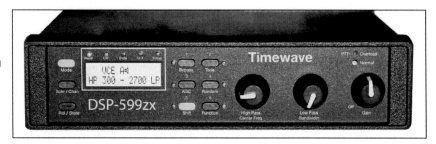

Fig 23: Adding digital signal processing can help with receiving RTTY

There will probably be somebody already running *MMTTY* in your area that you can ask too. You can even email me if you are desperate!

I will describe a basic setup for this program in the next chapter.

Receiving RTTY

To receive RTTY, the receiver needs to be stable and capable of good selectivity. In order to cope with crowded band occupancy, when contesting or chasing DX for example, the minimum you will need in IF selectivity is around 500Hz. If you have a 300 or even 250Hz IF filter, so much the better.

The AGC needs to be set to fast, and the speech processor needs to be off if you are using AFSK.

If you have a DSP filter as an add-on, it will help. The Timewave DXP599ZX (**Fig 23**) is a typical example of a very useful additional aid that can sort out some quite horrendous QRM problems! There are several add-on units like this that can enhance selectivity, reduce interference and can handle all modes

RTTY tuning

Tuning in an RTTY signal is a skill in itself. It is not like tuning in an SSB station where it is possible to have perfect copy on the transmitting station even though you might be anything up to 150Hz off frequency. You can even transmit back to that station with the same difference in frequency and be understood.

It does not matter what bandwidth you use for SSB, from 1.5kHz up to 3kHz and reception is still pretty good. You won't have to worry about additional selectivity at all.

However, you cannot hope to tune RTTY in the same manner. This is where most people fail to understand why they cannot read a RTTY signal. Having seen some new operators to the mode try to tune a signal, I cannot emphasise this point enough. It is extremely important to tune the signal correctly.

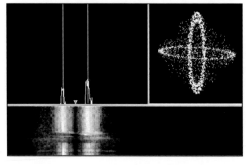

Fig 24: Tuning aids in the *MMTTY* software

In *MMTTY* you have two very useful tuning aids. These are shown in **Fig 24**. As you tune through an RTTY signal you will see the two tones as separate peaks. These will travel across the two vertical lines as you tune the transceiver. The secret is to line the two peaks with the two lines. At the same time, the

Lissajous scope display on the right should show two crossed ellipses, one horizontal and the other vertical. As you can see this shows a perfectly tuned RTTY signal. It also shows a notch filter set in the middle of the passband. This is very useful to null out any interference between the two tones.

Also within *MMTTY* there is a bandpass filter. Running with both of these selected will enhance copy.

Macros

Macros are pre-formed messages that can be sent at full speed when invoked. They are used a lot in contesting, but can also be very useful in everyday operation.

Setting macros is somewhat tedious, but they can save a lot of time when calling DX stations etc.

There are several within *MMTTY* to configure, sixteen of which show as buttons on the display (**Fig 25**). Full details on how to compose your own are in the Help file. There is more on using Macros in the next chapter.

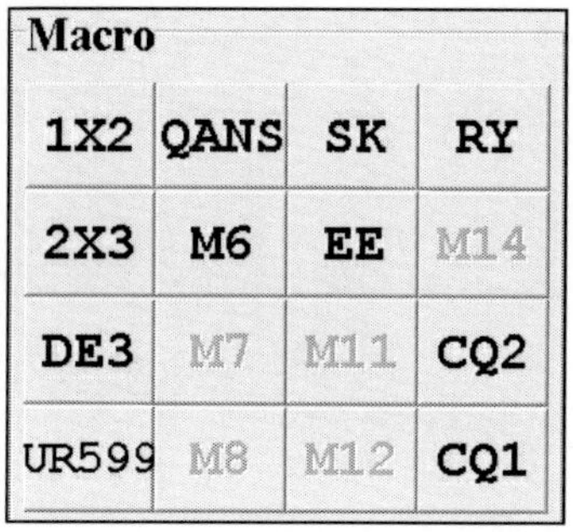

Macro			
1X2	QANS	SK	RY
2X3	M6	EE	M14
DE3	M7	M11	CQ2
UR599	M8	M12	CQ1

Fig 25: The MMTTY macro buttons

I personally feel that using macros takes away the spontaneity of a good conversation, so I tend to type each response in the bottom window - the type-ahead buffer - as I am receiving in the top window. Once you have finished commenting this way, the whole block of text can be sent at full speed. This is a much better way to converse.

CAT control

Most of the modern interfaces allow computer control of the transceiver. This is a very useful function to have, especially when contesting or DXing. Functions such as mode and frequency, band changes and so on are all controlled by the program, leaving just the tuning to the operator. When entering the parameters into the program, it is only necessary to select your transceiver, serial port and baud rate. It might also be necessary to specify whether DTR/RTS is needed for PTT or if Xon/Xoff flow control is used.

Once you have the radio set correctly, an interface working properly, with CAT control, and *MMTTY* on the screen and working, you will find that it is a real pleasure to operate RTTY. You have the type-ahead buffer, and also the ability to send larger files if you so desire, so the program is very versatile. With a suitable choice of macro settings you can work DX stations with two or three clicks on the buttons!

References

[1]   http://www.aa5au.com/rtty_radios.html
[2]   http://www.buxcomm.com/catalog/index.php
[3]   http://w3yy.com/fsk.htm
[4]   http://www.microham.com/
[5]   http://www.g4zlp.co.uk/
[6]   http://hamsoft.ca/pages/mmtty.php

[7]   http://www.cqham.ru/soundint.htm
[8]   http://aa5au.com/gettingstarted/rtty_start10.htm
[9]   http://uk.groups.yahoo.com/
[10] http://www.bartg.org.uk/

Operating an RTTY station

BY NOW YOU SHOULD HAVE downloaded *MMTTY* from the CD with this book, or from the web) and have your interface set up too. You will be ready to have some contacts using RTTY once you have configured the program parameters and set it up for your station.

MMTTY is not the only program that you can use, so look on the Internet for some more and see which one appeals to you the most. *MMTTY* is the most popular however, as I have pointed out, so the following description assumes you will be using that software.

When *MMTY* has finished installing and runs for the first time, you have to enter your call sign. You should have a desktop icon to click on to run the program. Next you should see a display on your screen similar to Fig 3.5 in chapter 3. Looking at the taskbar at the top you will see 'Option'. Click on that and select the bottom choice which is 'Setup'. This will bring you to **Fig 26**. Starting at the right hand side, 'Soundcard', select the soundcard relevant to your installation. This will depend on what interface you are using. Then go to 'Misc' and select the TX port. Again this will be dependant on your interface. In my case I am using the Microham II Keyer so have selected the third option. The other

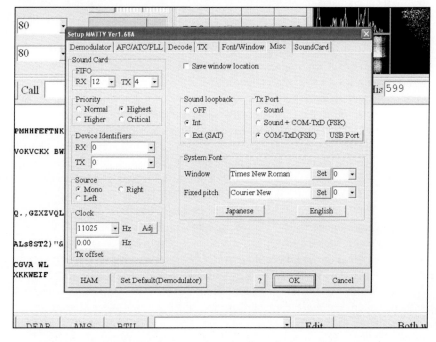

Fig 26: The Setup window on *MMTTY*

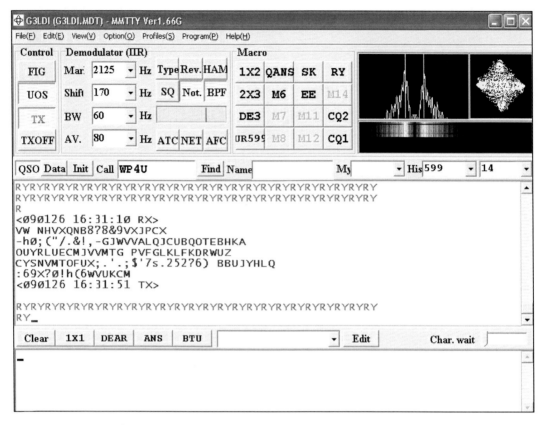

Fig 27: *MMTTY* running successfully

important parameter to set is the port for PTT and FSK. Check 'TX' to select this port. Then make sure the default Baud rate of 45.45 is selected in 'Decode'.

More detailed information is in the Help file or the lengthy and excellent instructions to be found on the AA5AU web site. [1]

Looking at the screen in **Fig 27**, you can see that the program is running and is set up with a Mark frequency of 2125Hz, with a shift of 170Hz. The large window with RYRYR in red is the received text and the window at the bottom is the transmitted text. This can be used while receiving, making for a very fast interchange of information, answering points as they are being received. All you do then is to hit the TX button to transmit the text. You can follow the progress as the text is being sent.

Just above the received text window are the details of the station you are working. Clicking on the call and his name in the received text window will insert the information into the log for you, the line just above the received text window. The log stays in *MMTTY* but can be easily transferred to other logging programs, or exported in various formats, including ADIF, and Cabrillo. However, some well known logging programs, *Logger32* for example, already has *MMTTY* built in, so you could use *MMTTY* within *Logger32*. This would be a much better way of using RTTY and logging it at the same time.

You can also set up the logging within *MMTTY* to be used in a contest, although there are more elegant ways of contesting which are described in a later chapter.

Macro	Long example
1 x 2call	VK9xx de G3LDI G3LDI AR PSE KN
RESPONSE	VK9xx QSL RST 599 599 KN
ACK	QSL 73 DE G3LDI TU
CQ	CQ CQ CQ DE G3LDI G3LDI G3LDI AR PSE K
RY	RYRYRYRYRYRYRYRYRYRYRYRYRYRYRY
LONG ANS	VK9xx DE G3LDI QSL YOUR RST IS 599 599 NAME IS ROGER AND QTH IS NORWICH AR KN

Table 2: *MMTTY* macro written in long hand . . .

Macro	Abbreviated example
1 x 2call	%C DE %M %M AR PSE KN\
RESPONSE	%C QSL UR %R %R %R KN\
ACK	QSL DE %M TU\
CQ	CQ CQ CQ DE %M %M %M AR PSE K\
RY	RYRYRYRYRYRYRYRYRYRYRYRYRYRYR#
LONG ANS	%C DE %M QSL UR %R %R NAME IS ROGER AND QTH IS NORWICH AR KN\

Table 3: . . . and in abbreviated form

Macros

There are macros which send standard text when you click on them, In order to have a slick operation, there is another series of macros that are programmable. These are in the boxes M1 to M16, plus another set just above the type ahead window, and even more in the pull down box in that row. Programmed correctly, you can enter the call into the call box and have a macro call that station for you, just by clicking on it. This is very useful when calling a DX station in a pile-up. Other macros can be programmed as you wish. Don't overdo it though. It gets very boring hearing all about your life history and the name of Aunt Nellie's cat! In the help file there is a section on how to program macros. Read these carefully before starting.

Macro example

MMTTY uses different keyboard characters for programming macros. They each have a dedicated meaning and you can make up messages using a mixture of these characters and plain text.

Group 1 macros are the 16 buttons to the left of the tuning display. The four group 2 macros are in the transmit window and are the ones most frequently used. You can find more details on programming and setting these up in the *MMTTY* Help file.

Table 2 shows a macro written in long hand, whilst **Table 3** shows the same thing using abbreviations such as those shown in **Table 4**. They will transmit exactly the same information. This is assuming that his call has been clicked on to transfer it to the log window.

%c	Your call
%m	his call
%r	his report
\	switch to receive
#	repeat macro

Table 4: Common abbreviations used in the macro example

Actually the macros work just as well when written in full. There are lots more to be found in the program. Right click on any of the macros and you will see another window showing that macro. There will also be a box labelled 'Commands'. If you click on that you will see a list of them. They are fairly intuitive once you have used them a few times.

These can form the basis of a personal selection. A description of the station, a list of your gear and antennas etc, are what we used to call a 'brag tape'. In the early days of machinery, we had an auto sender and a punched tape loop with all the station information on it, but a software macro is much more reliable and versatile, not to mention quieter!

Again, in the *MMTTY* manual, you will find various shortcut symbols for most of the above, like the call, name and so on, so the macro can be quite short.

I like to use a row of 'RY' to just help with final antenna tuning, or as a test transmission for somebody checking their receive capability. Incidentally, rows of 'RY' were used in the early days of RTTY in order to set up a polar relay in the terminal unit, as well as checking the actual teleprinter's adjustments. Bias distortion on the relay would lead to misprints and hence bad decoding. Rs and Ys were used because the two letters are a complete reversal of bits.

Tuning RTTY

In the *MMTTY* window, there are two methods of tuning. The two vertical lines represent the two tones, 2125 and 2275Hz. Assuming you have connected the interface correctly and set up the soundcard in the PC, depending on what interface you are using, you should see noise on the display. Tuning the signal in, you should be able to peak the two tones to align with the two vertical lines. At the same time, the scope patterns should be a cross, horizontal and vertical, a typical Lissajous pattern (see **Fig 28**).

This will take you a few attempts to get it correct but eventually you should be able to tune very quickly. Being a musician like myself does help, as I can normally tune without looking at the display, just by listening to the audio tones.

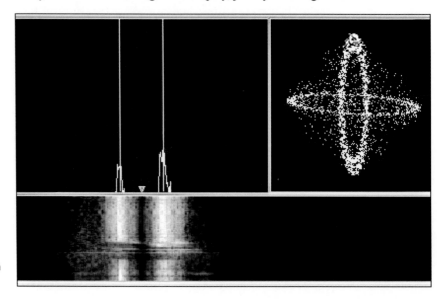

Fig 28: The two tools in *MMTTYY* to help you to accurately tune in RTTY signals

To help with reception, you can switch the bandpass filter on, and also the notch filter. The BPF is switched on by clicking on the BPF button and similarly the notch filter is set to on by clicking the NOT button. To place it in the centre of the two tones, you will have to click on the centre of the two lines. This increases the selectivity as an addition to having the receiver set to narrow bandwidth, normally 500Hz, but 250Hz if in a busy situation.

If you have everything set correctly and you are still not receiving, check the squelch level, the SQ button and the bargraph in green. The level can be adjusted by moving the line with the mouse. Check that the receiver is in LSB RTTY. You could be 'upside down' as described earlier. A quick check would be to click on the REV button to see if that makes copy legible. You can then correct the parameter causing the problem.

DX stations

Working DX stations is quite easy with RTTY. Most DX stations work split. Assuming you have a separate VFO or sub receiver in the transceiver, make sure that the same parameters are programmed into the second VFO. LSB and RTTY must be there or you will not be transmitting RTTY. Select split and monitor your transmission to make sure that RTTY is being used. The DX station will indicate where he is listening so monitor until you are sure what is happening.

Try to do more listening than transmitting. This will allow you to learn a lot about the mode. Working a DX station who is running a pile-up is a two button or macro situation.

When you are in contact with another station in a chat situation, the type ahead buffer can be used to program a reply and then clicking on the TX button sends it at full speed. If you cannot type too well, the buffer can speed the contact along nicely nicely, and RTTY always decodes that much better at full 'machine' speed, hence the reason for using 'diddles' as explained earlier.

When receiving weak or fluttery signals, copy can be difficult. Within *MMTTY* there are several profiles that can be selected to cope with varying conditions. Click on Profile and you will find four different ones already there to choose from, plus you can also add to these with other profiles. A selection of useful profiles can be found on the web at [2]. Documentation for the parameters that can be set in a profile is available at [3].

Logging and contesting are both possible in *MMTTY*, although there are more dedicated programs around that are more suitable (see the CD). The logging window is just above the received text window and is straightforward to use. You will find a number of tutorials on *MMTTY* on various web sites, but one of the most popular is that found on the AA5AU RTTY Page [4].

Useful software for DX working

The CD accompanying this book has a list of software for DX working, and copies of some of them. All these programs will involve a certain amount of configuration and setting up, but they are normally accompanied by a comprehensive help file. Most will interface with modern transceivers and a PC soundcard. Also, bear in mind that some programs are free, whereas others you have to pay for and register. You do, however, normally get a 30 day trial period.

References

[1]   http://www.aa5au.com/gettingstarted/GettingStartedOnRtty.html
[2]   http://www.dxlabsuite.com/winwarbler/Profiles/UserPara.ini
[3]   http://www.dxlabsuite.com/winwarbler/Profiles/UserPara.doc
[4]   http://www.aa5au.com/gettingstarted/rtty_start5.htm

5

Getting set up for PSK

PSK31 WAS DESIGNED BY Peter Martinez, G3PLX, as a chat mode mainly and an alternative to RTTY, although based on that mode of operation [1]. It was essentially aimed at keyboard to keyboard communication using low power whilst utilising a very narrow bandwidth (**Fig 29**), allowing about fifty contacts to take place within the bandwidth of an SSB transmission.

The full ANSI character set is used, permitting almost all written languages to be used, including Russian and Japanese and also allows correction whilst typing. That can be seen by both participants of the contact.

PSK31 uses phase-shift keying, in which a code symbol is signalled by a defined shift in the phase of the carrier, usually by 180 degrees [2]. See the box below for a more detailed explanation.

As the name of the mode implies, it works at 31.25 Bauds. One of the main attractions of PSK31 is that users are encouraged to run no more than 25 watts and it really has been quite successful in that aim. Running high power just spoils it for others.

Since Peter designed PSK31 there have been variations developed by others and although not used extensively, they are to be found in most programs now. PSK63 and PSK125 are available in most software programs. They do take up more bandwidth, however, and although they are occasionally used, most people seem to stay with PSK31. It is quite

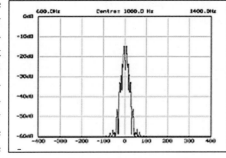

Fig 29: A spectral display showing how little space BPSK-mode PSK31 occupies. Picture from EA2BAJ's PSK31 web site [3]

PSK is a digital modulation scheme that conveys data by changing, or modulating, the phase of a reference signal. RTTY uses two tones 170Hz apart to convey information whereas PSK uses a finite number of phases, each assigned a unique pattern of binary digits. Usually, each phase encodes an equal number of bits. Each pattern of bits forms the symbol that is represented by the particular phase. The demodulator, which is designed specifically for the symbol-set used by the modulator, determines the phase of the received signal and maps it back to the symbol it represents, thus recovering the original data. There are a few variations of PSK. Normally, amateurs use BPSK, Binary Phase Shift Keying, which uses two phases, separated by 180°. The other basic system is QPSK, Quadrature Phase Shift Keying which uses four phases, separated by 90°.

35

Table 5: The HF
frequencies used
for PSK31

160m	1.838MHz	20m	14.070MHz	10m	28.120MHz
80m	3.580MHz	17m	18.100MHz	6m	50.250MHz
40m	7.040MHz	15m	21.070MHz		
30m	10.140MHz	12m	24.920MHz		

fast enough really and is about the average typing speed of 50WPM. As the mode was originally designed for chatting, it really is all that is needed. However, there are a few contests for PSK now and obviously the keen contester is going to take advantage of the higher Baud rate. The problem with that is when higher speeds are used, the more bandwidth the transmission takes, thus crowding out the lower speed stations. This, coupled with some stations using high power, has led to some heated debates!

Where to find PSK

Working with PSK requires a different technique from RTTY. PSK transmissions take place on one spot on each band as can be seen in **Table 5**.

These frequencies are all that you need to remember for HF operation and there is no tuning to be done on the transceiver at all. Setting the transceiver on these spot frequencies in USB is all that is needed. Just make sure that you have the full bandwidth selected for USB (no need for narrow filters on this mode as the filtering is done by the software), and the speech processor is *off*. Unlike RTTY, where you have the AGC set to fast, when using PSK, set the AGC to slow. Once you have done that, you can lock the VFO and use the software.

Software

There are quite a few software programs available for PSK and a number of links are on the CD associated with this book. *HamRadioDeluxe* is one which will not only cater for both PSK and RTTY, but it can be used for contesting also. *MixW* is another that will do a similar job, although this has to be purchased.

If you are keen on keeping your station log on the computer, as most people seem to do these days, try something like *Logger32* (which is also on the CD).

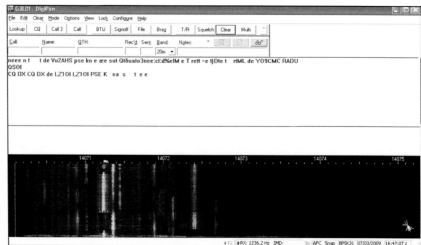

Fig 30: Screen shot
of the *Digipan*
software

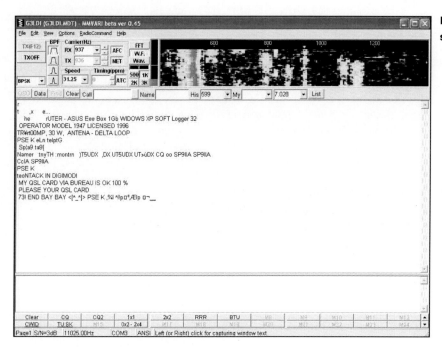

Fig 31: The main screen of *MMVARI*

This will not only cope with your station log, but will run RTTY using *MMTTY* and PSK using *ZAKANAKA*. One of the most used programs is *Digipan*, a screen shot of which can be seen in **Fig 30**.

Another program that will run PSK31 (as well as many other modes) is *MMVARI* (**Fig 31**), written by the same author as *MMTTY*. With the increased interest in contesting using PSK, *MMVARI* is used within the *N1MM* contest program (described in a later chapter). Using *N1MM* in data contests, it is very easy to change from RTTY using *MMTTY* to PSK using *MMVARI*. Various parameters have to be set up of course within *N1MM* and also *MMVARI*, but once done, they are rarely touched again. All of these programs can be found on the CD.

Tuning PSK stations

Receiver parameters are somewhat different for PSK. Start by placing your radio in the upper sideband (USB) mode. That's the convention that's been adopted by most PSK31 users throughout the world.

PSK31 signals have a distinctive warbly type of sound unlike any other digital mode. You won't find PSK31 by tuning around the bands like you do for RTTY. PSK signals sound like high-pitched warbling carriers and they all exist in one SSB bandwidth of spectrum. Tuning onto a PSK31 signal, like anything else, takes practice. In order to resolve PSK transmissions, set your receiver on one of the spot frequencies in Table 5 using USB and don't touch the tuning dial any more Assuming you have installed *Digipan* and filled in the required data before you start, and configured it correctly, you should see several stations on the waterfall display within the 3kHz passband. Clicking on any one of these should provide readable text within the RX window.

If you have the AFC button/checkbox selected in your program it will track the incoming PSK31 signal and in most cases adjust your transmit audio frequency accordingly. Depending on the propagation and both your transceiver stability, and the transmitting station's stability, you may find yourself and your contact chasing each other about.

In *MMVARI* there is a NET button which essentially locks your transmit audio frequency while still allowing the AFC on the receive signal. I normally keep NET on all the time when calling CQ, so that I stay where I started, and the other stations can work me without having to follow me about. Switching NET off again allows a split operation effectively. This technique is also useful for those situations where you need to work a DX station in split mode - you can do it without having to use the radio's split mode.

IMD measurement

Over-driving the transmitter can produce severe distortion so it is very important that the transmit drive level is set correctly. When looking at the waterfall display in the program you are using, all the stations should look roughly the same, just like the ones in Fig 30. If you compare these to the display shown in *MMVARI* in Fig 31, you can see just how much they vary when looking at a sample on the air.

When looking at a station that is just idling, with only the two tones and no transmitted text, you should see just two lines. I call them lines, but the display looks like a railway track really. If you see more than two lines, it means that the signal is wider than it should be. This indicates that the station's transmitter is distorting the PSK signal. The extra unwanted lines are known as the intermodulation distortion (IMD) product.

A standard test for measuring IMD is called a 'two tone test'. A PSK transmission in the idle situation is an ideal two-tone test itself so measurements can be taken on an idling transmitter. It is widely assumed that a very good IMD report for an idling signal is around -30db, a poor report around -20db with the worst possible at -10db. If the lines are not visible, the IMD readout is telling you simply that the signal is that many dB above the noise.

If you look at **Fig 32** you can see a example of a nice clean signal, weak, but the railway lines are obvious and it looks good. Moving to **Fig 33** you can

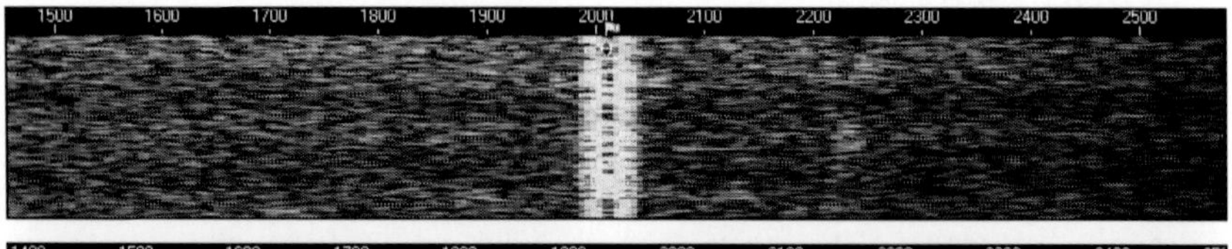

Fig 32: Good IMD performance

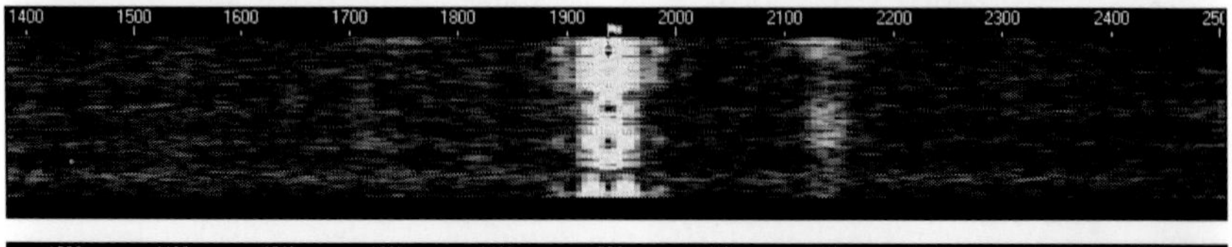

Fig 33: Poor IMD performance

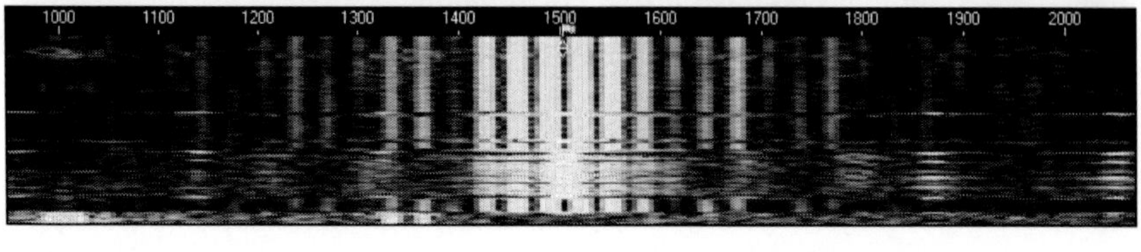

Fig 34: Very bad IMD performance

clearly see the IMD products on either side. It is overdriven and if you look at the display, this signal is occupying about 150Hz of spectrum. The modulation is not a clearly defined railway track, it more like two strong lines with lots of echo. This station is also wasting some of his modulation by spreading out the RF energy across more spectrum than needed, so the desired BPSK modulation is less efficient, not to mention causing problems for others. Finally look at **Fig 34**. I have seen signals like this, not too often, but it usually is someone new to the mode who has little idea how to adjust his gear. This signal takes up a large percentage of the 3kHz the PSK has to reside within.

This is arguably the most important aspect of PSK transmissions and great care should be taken to avoid IMD products. Setting up your transmitter properly before transmitting is therefore essential in this mode.

To adjust your transmitter, make sure that your processor is switched off, then switch the meter on its front panel to read ALC. Your transceiver manual will tell you how to do this. Then advance the audio level while monitoring the ALC. Just as the meter starts to read ALC, stop and then reduce the audio to the point where there is no ALC indication. It should then be reasonably clean, but obtain a report from a station whilst your transmitter is idling. You should always take pride in radiating as clean a signal as you can.

Be aware, however, that some computers, high RF fields or even your own soundcard can produce lines on the spectral display. so make sure it is the transmitting station who is offending before accusing him!

There is a lot of information available on this subject on various sites on the Internet. For instance, take a look at [4].

PSK31 operating

PSK31 is a good mode for just 'listening'. It is amazing what you can learn just by listening to two-way contacts, nets, or DX contacts. Try this for a while before you transmit. Even before using a soundcard or interface, have a look at a YouTube presentation on PSK31 by Randy, K7AGE. He has produced several of these and they can be very instructive [5].

PSK31 performance is the same when calling, listening or in contact, so it's easy to progress from listening to calling CQ, then to two-way contacts and multi-way nets. The narrow bandwidth and good weak-signal performance make it an ideal mode for low power stations, and it is quite amazing to see the amount of DX that gathers on this mode.

Interfacing

How do you get on the air with PSK31? Basically, three things are needed: audio to the computer soundcard to receive; audio from the computer to the transceiver to transmit and a method of controlling the PTT. A home-made interface can be used here similar to the one used for RTTY and a ready made interface unit, such as described earlier for RTTY will also suffice for PSK31.

There are a couple of things to remember about the really simple home made interface units. You can easily run into problems with earth loops and hum if there is no isolation using transformers. Always use screened leads, too. Great care should be taken when setting the audio level from the soundcard to the transceiver's microphone input. There might be a need for an attenuator here.

The better commercial units, such as the MicroHam MicroKeyer II won't suffer from any of these problems. Some, including the MicroHam, will even have their own soundcard. The MicroHam unit has a ready made cable set which is available for a range of transceivers.

If you are using one of these interfaces, you should remember to turn off the computer's sounds, or you may have beeps and other sounds going out over the air!

Setting up macros is very similar to that described earlier for RTTY, and instructions and guidelines are usually within the Help file of the software you might be using. When using PSK31 in the RSGB CC contests (see the next chapter), the same macros can be used for both modes. You will soon build up some experience on the mode and be able to type a reply while watching an in-coming message with the ability to correct any mistakes before they are sent out.

Finally, a word about grounding. *All* units should be tied to a common ground to avoid ground loop problems. You may have to use some ferrite rings or beads on audio leads, or put small capacitors across the microphone socket and the audio input into the sound card. This applies to *all* data modes.

And finally

This book is just to get you started and there is not enough space to fully cover every possible combination of software and hardware. So, have fun and enjoy PSK31.

References

[1]   http://www.qsl.net/wm2u/psk31.html (Interfacing plus links to many PSK sites).
[2]   http://hamradio.arc.nasa.gov/meetings/PSK31presentation.html (PSK theory with several screen shots of *Digipan*).
[3]   http://aintel.bi.ehu.es/psk31.html
[3]   http://www.mymorninglight.org/ham/psk.htm
[4]   http://www.youtube.com/watch?v=jQpBGh9RMEQ,
      http://www.youtube.com/watch?v=ZaAXMzGIUGA
      (Randy K7AGE basic PSK tutorial)

6

Contests, clubs and cards

THERE ARE NUMEROUS RTTY and PSK (sometimes referred to as 'datamodes' or just 'data') contests in the calendar. Although PSK was not devised originally as a contest mode, the popularity of the mode seems to have encouraged PSK enthusiasts to use it in contesting. However, RTTY certainly has made an enormous growth in amateur radio contesting, particularly since it is now so easy to use the mode with computers.

Contests are fun. That is the prime aim of any contest. They encourage entrants to stretch themselves and their stations to the limit. Contests are all about efficient operation; they test your operating skills to the extreme, not to mention your patience and knowledge. You have to cope with adverse conditions, lots of stations close to each other so it helps to have an efficient station. HF contests create and renew friendships among participants and it's always fun to see how others are doing. All this applies equally to data contests as those for other modes. As a starting point, read the article *A Beginner's Guide to RTTY Contesting* which can be found on the CD that accompanies this book.

Take a look over the RTTY segment of a band when a major contest is in progress and you will find there are thousands of stations active. Because of this, as with other world wide events, the bandplans do suffer somewhat and activity is heard well outside the suggested allocations. There are so many RTTY stations active during a contest and there is a very limited section of each band normally allocated for RTTY.

RTTY is a much snappier mode too, with exchanges taking a minimum amount of time. In contests RTTY must be the easiest mode to use; it is quite possible to operate seriously in a contest and eat a meal at the same time!

PSK31 on the other hand is a slower mode in change-over; stations on the PSK31 frequency all have to occupy the 3kHz audio bandwidth and a lot of those there may not be in the contest. If you call and they are not in the contest themselves they will assume you want to chat and will send a macro with a huge amount of unwanted information. This takes up valuable time when you just want a contest exchange. Indeed, PSK31 was not designed for contests; it was intended purely as a chat mode.

Some major contests are as long as 48 hours, and not many people can afford that amount of time, nor would they wish to do so. However, you don't have to be *in* a contest to participate in it. You can take part and cherry-pick the new countries that you need on the mode, or just spend a few hours having fun, handing out points, or just practice your contesting skills. For more information on the contests available, take a look at the various Contest Calendar sites online [1, 2, 3].

Fig 35: A wall plaque

Most of the international contests are 48-hour events, some last 24 hours. However, if you wish to start in a small way try the RSGB CC Cumulative contests. These events only last 90 minutes and are an ideal place for a beginner to start. It might just be enough to encourage you to try longer ones. They run from February until July and alternate CW, SSB and Data. The Data section is a mixed event, using both RTTY and PSK31, so strategy is needed here for competitors because a mixture of both modes is needed to obtain a good score. More details, together with a lot more general information about contesting, can be found on the RSGB web site [1]. There is also a *CC Newsletter* that you can sign up for at [4] to keep you informed.

Actually there is nothing in the rules of most contests that force the operator to use PSK31 or 45.45 Baud RTTY. It would help to speed things up a lot if operators tried using PSK63 and 75 Baud RTTY. BARTG do run two 75 Baud RTTY contests per year, one in April and the other in September, both of which are only four hours long. They are becoming very popular and will help hone your keyboard skills!

Even some of the longer international contests have six hour slots that can be useful, or you could try a single band entry. Propagation could limit your on-air time and you might still win something! The SARTG contest on New Year's Day is only a few hours long and is on just two bands, 80 and 40 metres. There are lots of others; just check the contest calendars mentioned above.

Wall plaques and certificates are up for grabs in all sorts of categories in the major events and it is very satisfying to win something to display on your shack wall.

Club education

Local radio clubs will normally have evenings dedicated to instruction in getting started on data modes. If yours does not, suggest that it go on the club's programme. It is an ideal way of gaining information, sorting out problems and so on. In our club we have workshop evenings, where a station will be set up and a complete demonstration of RTTY, PSK31, contest programs and so on will be on the screen. A picture can sometimes be worth a thousand words and also being interactive can be very helpful.

Some clubs have activity evenings on the air, with two way contacts taking place to test the modes or contest programs and macros. Details of your local radio club can be found at [5] or [6]

If you are keen on data modes, consider joining BARTG (the British Amateur Radio Teledata Group) [7]. BARTG is free to join and members are always willing to help with any problems you might have with any data mode. BARTG also has tutorials on its web site, plus lots of related links, lists of available awards and sample sounds to identify other data modes.

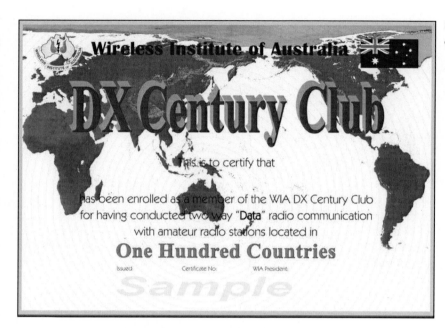

Fig 36: a certificate of achievement

QSL cards, awards and DX

There are awards available for both RTTY and PSK31, especially from BARTG. You can use QSL cards that you have collected. Alternatively, it is possible to use virtual QSLs from Logbook of the World (LoTW) [8] after submitting your log or logs to the ARRL for checking purposes. The logs can be from your normal operating or from any contest in which you may have participated.

Data specific awards can also be won from other organisations such as ARRL, *CQ Magazine*, and many others from various national radio societies. They will usually accept 'real' QSL cards the hard way, or a shortcut method such as LoTW (see below for more about this). I prefer the old method as you do get some very attractive and worthwhile cards to keep. However, for a very quick award win, BARTG will accept a contest log, so if you work a certain number of countries in a contest, that log will bring you an award. Check out the BARTG web site for details [7].

If you are keen and lucky enough, you may win a wall plaque (**Fig 35**). These are normally sponsored, either by clubs or individuals. Certificates, such as the one shown in **Fig 36,** are more prolific and are cheaper because wall plaques will cost the applicant money unless they are sponsored.

If you are into chasing DX, join LoTW (Logbook of The World) [8]. As a registered user of this electronic QSLing system, you can apply for DXCC awards and endorsements. You can link your DXCC record to your LoTW account so that you can track your progress online. Users can view the DXCC matrix or for a quick glance at what has been earned and what is needed. LoTW displays DXCC credits for Mixed, Phone, CW, RTTY (digital), bands and DXCC Challenge.

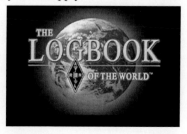

Club Log, written and maintained by Michael Wells, G7VJR, is another useful database system to belong to. Club Log is a web-based system for DXers to upload their ADIF log files. Any radio amateur in the world with an electronic log can sign up. Like other systems, notably LoTW, Club Log then imports the content of those files into a large, central database.

The most well-known feature of Club Log is the expedition tools, which provide a slot-chasing system as part of an expedition log search page, with propagation and activity suggestions and a free online QSL request system. This facility has been used by high-profile expeditions like FT5GA, K4M, T32C, VP8ORK, K5D and many others. However, although this is understandably the most prominent part of Club Log (receiving over 6 million visitors per year) it is only a tiny part of the overall project.

Uploads to LoTW and Club Log can be automated from within *Logger32*. Most modern amateurs now use an electronic log and *Logger32* is a very popular one. There are others of course, but *Logger32* is especially useful for RTTY and PSK in that these data modes are built in, using *MMTTY* and *MMVARI*.

Using all three of these facilities greatly reduces the 'officework' when chasing DX and awards. *Logger32* is on the CD supplied with this book.

Email-based forums - reflectors - can be very helpful too and the RTTY contest reflector is one such site. You can sign up to receive emails or read the archives at [9]. Topics may include contest operating, contest score posting with soapbox, DXing, software, other digital modes.

To make your life easier by finding out the latest RTTY/PSK stations, DX-peditions and so on, log onto a DXCluster. An internet search will show a list of these useful real-time DX reporting sites. You can stay connected whilst you are operating as there is no time-out.

Having said all of this, there is nothing like fishing! Just get on the band and call CQ. Have a chat on the keyboard. This can be just as enjoyable and you can also learn a lot.

Contest software

There are many contest programs available; some you pay for, some are free. For instance there is *Writelog, N1MM, CT, Winlog, MixW* etc (see the CD with this book).

One of the most popular in use these days is *N1MM*. A bonus is that it's free! It uses the *MMTTY* engine and is quite a sophisticated package. Setting it up is beyond the scope of this book, but here is a rough starter.

Go to the *N1MM* site [10], download and install the main program, reading the instructions on the site (or just use the copy on the CD that accompanies this book). You will then have to configure the *MMTTY* engine in order for it to work, plus you will have to configure the *N1MM* program itself. It would be best to try to get advice and guidance when doing that as it is a complicated procedure.

Once the program is running, the first thing to do is to fill in all your station details. Go to CONFIG, left click and you will see the Configurer screen come up. Go to the top and click on "Change your station data". Fill this in with all the relevant details and click OK.

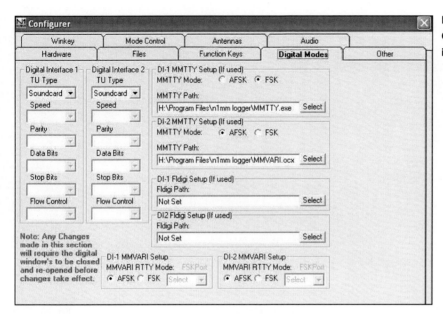

Fig 37: The Configurer screen in *N1MM*

To use the *MMTTY* engine in *N1MM*, first download it from [11] or use the version on the CD supplied with this book. Unzip it and put it into the root of *N1MM*. Then click on 'config', go to the top of the list to 'configure ports, mode control, audio, other', then click on 'digital modes' (**Fig 37**). Put the path to MMTTY in the window at the bottom.

Under TU type select 'soundcard' then select FSK or AFSK in the check-boxes provided and that should provide a starting point. If you are using the MicroHam II USB keyer, you will have loaded that up, and configured it, first. You will then see the MicroHam soundcard in that soundcard drop down menu, so select that.

Then, while the transceiver is in the RTTY mode, simply click Window/Digital Window and you should have instant RTTY. If you have any difficulty with this, please look at the AA5AU site [12] where there is a plethora of helpful information.

When operating contests with *N1MM* you will have to import the macros. Go to the main *N1MM* web site [13] and you will find many macros there to down-load, and you can alter them to suit your own station. Read the Help file and follow the instructions and you should be fine. There are several sets of suit-able macros on the CD associated with this book. However, there are set pro-tocols to follow with the macros, so if in doubt again ask. In fact, it will prob-ably be a good idea to have an experienced *N1MM* contester to send you some macros for various different contests. All you have to do is to make a macro directory under *N1MM* and store them all in there, importing them to the main program as needed.

Operating a RTTY contest could not be easier and you can eat a meal while running on 20 meters!

Within *N1MM* you can use both RTTY with the *MMTTY* engine and PSK with *MMVARI*. Switching between modes is simple to achieve. This is useful when operating in the RSGB CC data section which now involves both RTTY and

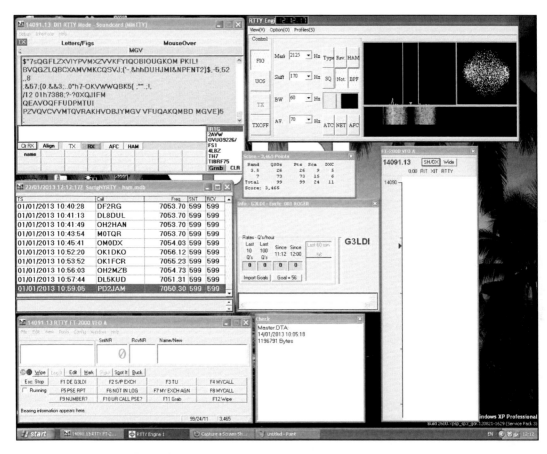

Fig 38: The main N1MM screen looks complex but can be rearranged to suit the user

```
START-OF-LOG: 2.0
ARRL-SECTION: DX
CALLSIGN: G3LDI
CLUB: Norfolk ARC
CONTEST: SARTGNYRTY
CATEGORY: SINGLE-OP-ASSISTED ALL LOW
CLAIMED-SCORE: 3465
OPERATORS: G3LDI
NAME: Roger Cooke
ADDRESS: The Old Nursery,
ADDRESS: The Drift, Swardeston,
ADDRESS: Norwich, Norfolk,  NR14 8LQ
ADDRESS: UK
CREATED-BY: N1MM Logger V12.12.2
SOAPBOX: Not sure if it was necessary to include name in the
exchange but most people were doing just that
QSO: 3589 RY 2013-01-01 0801 G3LDI    0001 ROGER K4GMH   599 0001
QSO: 3589 RY 2013-01-01 0801 G3LDI    0002 ROGER OK1MSP  599 0001
QSO: 3589 RY 2013-01-01 0802 G3LDI    0003 ROGER DL5KUD  599 0001
QSO: 3589 RY 2013-01-01 0803 G3LDI    0004 ROGER DJ2IA   599 0002
QSO: 3589 RY 2013-01-01 0803 G3LDI    0005 ROGER DJ4MH   599 0001
QSO: 3589 RY 2013-01-01 0804 G3LDI    0006 ROGER GM0FGI  599 0002
QSO: 3589 RY 2013-01-01 0806 G3LDI    0007 ROGER OH1TN   599 0004
END-OF-LOG:
```

Fig 39: A sample Cabrillo log exported from the N1MM software

PSK31, so it is necessary to switch between the two modes whilst maintaining a consecutive serial number.

Fig 38 shows a typical *N1MM* screen. Whilst this may look cluttered and unreadable, bear in mind that the image in this book is much smaller than it would be on your computer monitor! It is also possible to arrange these windows just as you want to see them and then save their positions so that every time *N1MM* opens it will appear just as you finished using it. This applies to the log too, so you won't ever lose any log entries.

N1MM will log and 'dupe' all calls and also keep a check on rates, multipliers and so on. There are other neat features, such as a bandmap, which can be populated with calls heard on what frequency. Clicking on them instantly returns the transceiver to that frequency. Telnet access to the DXCluster with similar functions is also available, plus lot of other features. When the contest is finished, a Cabrillo log is produced which should be checked and uploaded to the contest adjudicator. **Fig 39** shows an example of a Cabrillo file produced after the contest with a lot of the contacts removed (there's a full explanation of Cabrillo logs on the CD).

Search and pounce

If you've never operated a RTTY contest before then starting with 'search and pounce' is certainly easier than 'running'. I highly recommend getting started that way.

This is good experience as you wait and listen for a calling station and then jump in with your call sign (hit the F4 key) after his CQ. Then when you are recognized and have received his exchange, send your exchange by hitting F2 and the QSO will be logged. When you have his acknowledgement move on to the next station. Using search and pounce will help you get familiar with the way operators work the contest and to get a feel for the rhythm of RTTY contesting.

Running

To run successfully in a RTTY contest you will need a reasonably competent station. Running merely means occupying one frequency and calling CQ all the time. So if you have at least a small directional antenna or a fairly good vertical then you can give running a try.

Pressing F1 will send your CQ for you. When you see a call in the text window responding to you, click on it and it will appear in the log window. Press return to send the exchange, then click on his exchange and it will again transfer to the log window. Press return again and it is logged and you call CQ again, simple!

Of course you will need other macros set for repeat requests and so on plus there is a lot more you can do which will come with experience.

Reverse Beacon Network

It is now possible to use the Reverse Beacon Network to show RTTY and PSK spots, thanks to Walter Dallmeier, DL4RCK. This is a very useful feature which was only available for CW stations until Walter produced his skimmer software for data.

RCKskimmer [14] is able to search for digital signals (RTTY, PSK31, PSK63, etc,) in a FFT-spectrum of a standard receiver like K3, FT1000x, etc, or an SDR receiver with a NF-connection to the soundcard of the PC by using the *MMVARI* module. All bands and frequencies can be scanned in a row. All call signs with CQ, QRZ, DE or TEST are detected and listed with the exact Mark frequency by using the *OmniRig Transceiver Control* by Alex Shovkoplyas, VE3NEA. Not many will wish to run the skimmer software, but looking at the spots on the RBN (Reverse Beacon Network) [15] can be very useful.

The call signs are posted in real time to the RCK-DCS (Digital Cluster System) [16] that has been specially designed for *RCKskimmer* and accessible for everyone with the spots going also to the reverse beacon net network.

The future

It is impossible to say just what is around the corner, but each year brings something new in both hardware and software. Suffice it to say that we have come a long way since the humble beginnings of data, way back in the 1950s. If only some of those pioneers that are now 'silent keys' could see what we have today and if only we could look fifty years ahead! Every era of amateur radio has its attractions so enjoy the sophisticated scene that we have now and have fun!

References

[1]   http://www.rsgbcc.org/hf/ (RSGB HF Contesting Guide.)
[2]   http://www.hornucopia.com/contestcal/contestcal.html (General Contest Calendar).
[3]   http://www.bartg.org.uk/contests.asp (BARTG Contests)
[4]   http://www.rsgbcc.org/
[5]   List of RSGB affiliated clubs: http://www.rsgb.org/clubsandtraining/
[6]   *RSGB Yearbook*, RSGB. Published annually and available online from: http://www.rsgbshop.org
[7]   http://www.bartg.org.uk/
[8]   http://www.arrl.org/lotw (Logbook of the World)
[9]   http://lists.contesting.com/mailman/listinfo/RTTY
[10] http://www.n1mm.com (*N1MM* contest program)
[11] http://hamsoft.ca/pages/programmers/programmer-downloads.php (MMTTY Engine)
[12] http://aa5au.com/rtty.html (Numerous RTTY help pages)
[13] http://www.n1mm.hamdocs.com/
[14] http://www.walter-dallmeier.de/software-by-dl4rck/rckskimmer/
[15] http://www.reversebeacon.net/
[16] http://www.walter-dallmeier.de/software-by-dl4rck/rckskimmer/digital-cluster-system/